G000060423

Mental Arithmetic Success

Circle the odd one out.

650 + 8   608 + 50

680 + 5   618 + 40

$\frac{4}{8}$ 618

40

680    $\frac{2}{4}$

= ÷

+

- +

Write the next equivalent fraction.

$\frac{1}{2} = \frac{2}{4} = \frac{3}{6} = \frac{4}{8}$

Paul Broadbent

About this book

Mental arithmetic

Mental arithmetic involves carrying out calculations and working with numbers in your head, without the help of a calculator or computer. It is an important part of your child's education in maths and will help them to manage everyday situations in later life. This book will help your child to solve increasingly difficult problems in their head and at greater speed. It provides the opportunity to learn, practise and check progress in a wide range of mental arithmetic skills, such as addition, subtraction, multiplication, division and working with fractions, decimals and measures. This book will also aid preparation for the **Mental mathematics** paper in the Key Stage 2 National Curriculum Tests (also known as SATs).

Features of the book

Learn and revise – explains and refreshes mental arithmetic skills and strategies.

Practice activities – a variety of tasks to see how well your child has grasped each skill.

Mental arithmetic tests – 20 questions which test and reinforce your child's understanding of the preceding topics.

Speed tests and *Progress charts* – the one-minute tests challenge your child to carry out mental calculations at increasing speed and the progress charts enable them to record their results.

Key facts – a summary of key points that your child should learn by heart and memorise.

Answers are in a pull-out booklet at the centre of the book.

Mental arithmetic tips

- Cooking with your child provides opportunities to use measures – reading scales, converting between units and calculating with amounts.

- Look at prices and compare amounts when shopping. Use receipts to find differences between prices.

- Play board games, such as a simplified version of *Monopoly*, and dice games, such as *Yahtzee*, taking opportunities to add and subtract numbers and money.

- Addition and subtraction facts to 20 and the multiplication tables are basic key facts that your child will need to know so that they can solve problems with bigger numbers. Regularly practise these facts – you could write them on sticky notes around the house for your child to see or answer.

- Short, regular practice to build confidence is better than spending too long on an activity so that boredom creeps in. Keep each session to 20–30 minutes.

Contents

Counting and numbers

Some sequences have missing numbers. Look carefully at the numbers you are given and try to work out the numbers next to these first. Then you can write the others.

207 **208** _209_ _210_ _211_ **212** _213_

The missing numbers are 209, 210, 211 and 213.

Counting patterns can use steps of different numbers. To work out the steps, look at the difference between the numbers.

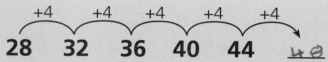

28 **32** **36** **40** **44** _48_

This is going up in fours. The next number is 48.

Practice activities

1. Write the missing numbers in each sequence.

   a) 93   94   _95_   _96_   97   98   _99_

   b) 108   _109_   110   111   _112_   _113_   114

   c) _379_   _380_   381   382   _83_   384   385

   d) 703   704   705   _706_   _707_   _708_   709

   e) 596   597   ____   ____   ____   601   602

2. Write the next number in each of these.

   a) 22   24   26   28   30   ____

   b) 120   130   140   150   160   ____

   c) 32   36   40   44   48   ____

   d) 150   200   250   300   350   ____

   e) 8   16   24   32   40   ____

3. Complete these sequences.

a) ____   ____   36   39   42   ____   ____

b) ____   ____   60   70   80   ____   ____

c) ____   ____   36   40   44   ____   ____

d) ____   ____   24   32   40   ____   ____

4. Write the missing numbers on each number line.

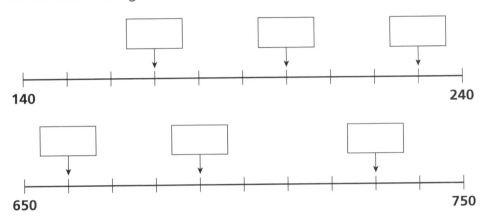

140   240

650   750

5. Continue these sequences.

a) 310   410   510   610   ____   ____   ____

b) 560   570   580   590   ____   ____   ____

c) 245   345   445   545   ____   ____   ____

d) 244   254   264   274   ____   ____   ____

6. On a number track, I start at 5 and count on in 3s.

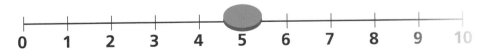

0   1   2   3   4   5   6   7   8   9   10

Will I land on 15? _____

7. Grace has between 20 and 30 books. She counted them in threes and there
was 1 left over. She then counted them in fours and there was still 1 left over.

How many books did she have in total? _____

Place value

Learn and revise

Look at this number and how it is made:

562 = 500 + 60 + 2

five hundred and sixty-two

Hundreds	Tens	Ones
5	6	2

$500 \rangle 60 \rangle 2 \rangle$

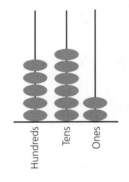

Make sure you look at the place of each digit in a number.

562 is very different from 625, even though it has the same digits.

Practice activities

1. Write the missing numbers.

    a) 285   ⟶   200   +   _____   +   5

    b) 617   ⟶   _____   +   10   +   7

    c) 354   ⟶   300   +   _____   +   _____

    d) 793   ⟶   _____   +   _____   +   3

    e) 198   ⟶   _____   +   90   +   _____

2. Write these as numbers.

    a) six hundred and thirty-eight   _____

    b) four hundred and seventeen   _____

    c) seven hundred and eighty   _____

    d) five hundred and three   _____

3. What numbers do each of these arrow cards show?

a) 400 ⟩ 30 ⟩ 7 ⟩ ____

b) 600 ⟩ 90 ⟩ 4 ⟩ ____

c) 900 ⟩ 10 ⟩ 8 ⟩ ____

d) 100 ⟩ 80 ⟩ 9 ⟩ ____

4. **a)** What number is 200 more than 525?   ____

b) What number is 60 more than 418?   ____

c) What number is 500 less than 803?   ____

d) What number is 70 less than 497?   ____

5. Write the numbers shown by each abacus.

a) 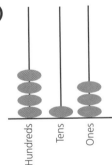 ____

b) 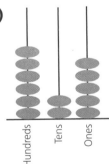 ____

c) 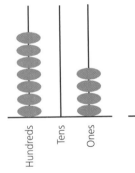 ____

6. Numbers can be partitioned in different ways. Complete these.

a) **58**

50 + 8

40 + 18

30 + ____

____ + 38

10 + ____

b) **63**

60 + 3

50 + ____

____ + 23

30 + ____

____ + 43

10 + ____

c) **47**

40 + ____

____ + 17

20 + ____

____ + 37

Comparing and ordering numbers

Learn and revise

< and > are used to compare numbers. Don't get them confused!

< means 'is less than'	> means 'is greater than'
135 < 214	368 > 309
135 is less than 214	368 is greater than 309

When you compare two numbers, you must look carefully at the value of the digits.

If you have a list of numbers to put in order, look at the place value of the digits, starting with the hundreds.

Example: Put these in order, starting with the smallest.

345   630   92   354   85   ⟶   85   92   345   354   630

Practice activities

1. Write < or > to make these correct.

    a) 75 _____ 83   b) 212 _____ 209

    c) 395 _____ 299   d) 507 _____ 509

2. Underline the smallest number in this set. Draw a circle around the largest.

3. Write each set of numbers in order of size, starting with the smallest.

    a) | 258   302   285   311 | _____ _____ _____ _____

    smallest

    b) | 568   600   589   509 | _____ _____ _____ _____

    smallest

    c) | 677   784   721   729 | _____ _____ _____ _____

    smallest

    d) | 476   467   674   647 | _____ _____ _____ _____

    smallest

Comparing and ordering numbers

4. Write any number that would be correct for these.

   a) 54 > _____ > 38

   b) 106 > _____ > 93

   c) 245 < _____ < 290

   d) 512 < _____ < 515

5. Here are the lengths of six of the longest rivers in the UK. Write them in order in the table, starting with the longest.

   River Clyde 172 km   **River Thames 346 km**

   River Severn 354 km   **River Trent 297 km**

   River Tay 188 km   **River Wye 215 km**

Name of river	Length (km)

Mental arithmetic test 1

1. Circle the smallest number in this set.

   342   331   299

       290   309

2. Make the largest possible number from these three digit cards.

   6 **8** **3**   ____ ____ ____

3. Write the missing numbers in this sequence.

   138   139   ____   141   142   ____

4. $487 = 400 +$ ____ $+ 7$

5. What number is 200 more than 308?

   ____

6. Write these weights in order, starting with the lightest.

   685 g   658 g   589 g   590 g   586 g

   ____ ____ ____ ____ ____

7. $695 =$ ____ $+$ ____ $+ 5$

8. What is the value of the circled digit?

   ⑦4 8   ____

9. Write the next two numbers in this sequence.

   30   36   42   48   ____ ____

10. Write < or > to make this correct.

    385 ____ 410

11. Write these numbers in order, starting with the smallest.

    532   325   253   352   523

    ____ ____ ____ ____ ____

12. $583 + 400 =$ ____

13. Write a number that would make this correct.

    $226 >$ ____ > 218

14. What number does this abacus show?

    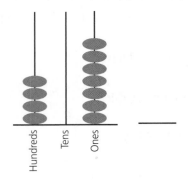

    ____

15. Write this using numerals:

    six hundred and eighty-one

    ____

16. On a number line you start at 1 and count on in 3s. Do you land on 20?

    Yes / No

17. Write the missing numbers.

    50   ____   150   200   ____   300

18. What is 100 more than 742? ____

19. Write the number 618 in words.

    _____

    _____

20. Write the missing numbers.

    ____ ____ 32 40 48 ____ ____

Score   /20

1. Write this using numerals:

five hundred and seven

_____

2. Write the missing numbers.

451 _____ _____ 454 455 _____

3. 319 = _____ + _____ + 9

4. What is 100 more than 654? _____

5. Write these lengths in order, starting with the longest.

385 cm   359 cm   358 cm
          258 cm   285 cm

_____ _____ _____ _____ _____

6. Write < or > to make this correct.

720 _____ 702

7. Write the number 389 in words.

_____

_____

8. What number does this abacus show?

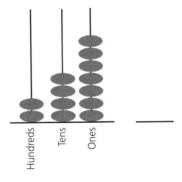

_____

9. A car travels 312 km on Monday and then a further 200 km on Tuesday. How far has it travelled altogether?

_____ km

10. What is the value of the circled digit?

6 ④ 5   _____

11. Draw beads on this abacus to show the number 324.

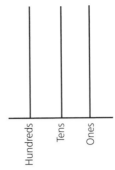

12. Write the next two numbers in this sequence.

325   425   525   625   _____   _____

13. 706 − 300 = _____

14. Write a number that would make this correct.

297 < _____ < 301

15. Write the missing numbers.

_____ _____ 40 44 48 _____ _____

16. What number do these arrow cards make?

600 + _____ + _____ = _____

17. What number is 200 less than 608?

_____

18. What number is ten times greater than 45?

_____

19. Write these numbers in order, starting with the smallest.

912   921   935   909   911

_____ _____ _____ _____ _____

20. I am thinking of a number. If I added 50 to the number, it would make 610. What number am I thinking of?

_____

Score   **/20**

11

Addition and subtraction facts

Learn and revise

Addition and subtraction are connected. Use any facts you know to help learn others.

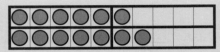

This shows that 6 + 7 = 13

How did you see this? Did you add 5 and 5 together, then 1 add 2? Or did you add 6 and 6, then add 1?

You can use the addition fact 6 + 7 to work out the subtraction facts:

6 + 7 = 13   13 − 6 = 7

7 + 6 = 13   13 − 7 = 6

Remember that subtraction is the inverse, or opposite, of addition.

Practice activities

1. Write the addition facts these show.

      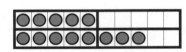

a) _____ + _____ = _____   b) _____ + _____ = _____   c) _____ + _____ = _____

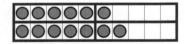   

d) _____ + _____ = _____   e) _____ + _____ = _____   f) _____ + _____ = _____

2. Use each addition fact to answer these.

a) **7 + 6 = 13**   6 + 7 = _____   13 − 6 = _____   13 − 7 = _____

b) **9 + 5 = 14**   5 + 9 = _____   14 − 9 = _____   14 − 5 = _____

c) **8 + 7 = 15**   7 + 8 = _____   15 − 7 = _____   15 − 8 = _____

d) **6 + 9 = 15**   9 + 6 = _____   15 − 6 = _____   15 − 9 = _____

Addition and subtraction facts

3. Use the doubles to help answer these.

a) [domino] 6 + 6 = _____   6 + 7 = _____   6 + 5 = _____

b) [domino] 8 + 8 = _____   8 + 9 = _____   8 + 7 = _____

c) [domino] 5 + 5 = _____   5 + 6 = _____   5 + 4 = _____

d) [domino] 7 + 7 = _____   7 + 8 = _____   7 + 6 = _____

e) [domino] 9 + 9 = _____   9 + 10 = _____   9 + 8 = _____

4. Answer these. Use the number lines to help if you need them.

a) 8 ⊢———————⊣ 15

15 – 8 = _____

b) 9 ⊢———————⊣ 18

18 – 9 = _____

c) 7 ⊢———⊣ 11

11 – 7 = _____

d) 8 ⊢———⊣ 14

14 – 8 = _____

e) 6 ⊢———————⊣ 13

13 – 6 = _____

f) 7 ⊢———————⊣ 16

16 – 7 = _____

5. Join these to the matching answers circled in red.

| 14 – 8 | 13 – 6 | 15 – 7 | 17 – 8 | 11 – 5 | 14 – 7 |

(6)   (7)   (8)   (9)

| 12 – 4 | 15 – 6 | 12 – 6 | 15 – 8 | 11 – 3 | 13 – 4 |

6. Write the missing numbers.

a) 5 + _____ = 11   b) 12 – _____ = 8   c) _____ + 9 = 20   d) _____ – 3 = 8

e) 7 + _____ = 13   f) 18 – _____ = 11   g) _____ + 7 = 19   h) _____ – 6 = 7

13

Addition

Learn and revise

Break numbers up so that you can add them in your head.

Example: What is 158 add 5?

$$158 + 5 =$$
$$100 + 50 + \underline{8 + 5} =$$
$$150 + \underline{13} = 163$$

Add the ones and then add this to the hundreds and tens.

Example: Add together 233 and 40.

$$233 + 40 =$$
$$200 + 30 + 3 + 40 =$$
$$200 + \underline{30 + 40} + 3 =$$
$$200 + \underline{70} + 3 = 273$$

Add the tens and then add this to the hundreds and then add on the ones.

Practice activities

1. Add these mentally and write the answers.

   a) $83 + 5$ = _____

   b) $27 + 6$ = _____

   c) $53 + 9$ = _____

   d) $91 + 5$ = _____

   e) $142 + 3$ = _____

   f) $229 + 6$ = _____

   g) $234 + 7$ = _____

   h) $348 + 9$ = _____

2. Now add these mentally and write the answers.

   a) $31 + 50$ = _____

   b) $64 + 30$ = _____

   c) $23 + 70$ = _____

   d) $51 + 40$ = _____

   e) $234 + 40$ = _____

   f) $127 + 50$ = _____

   g) $201 + 90$ = _____

   h) $329 + 60$ = _____

3. Complete these addition grids.

a)

+	30	60	20	50
134	164			
211				
302				

b)

+	200	300	500	400
123	323			
307				
528				

4. Colour the star that is the odd one out in each set.

a)

| 305 + 20 | 320 + 5 | 300 + 25 | 350 + 20 |

b)

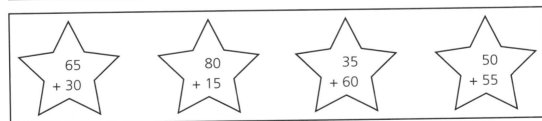

| 65 + 30 | 80 + 15 | 35 + 60 | 50 + 55 |

c)

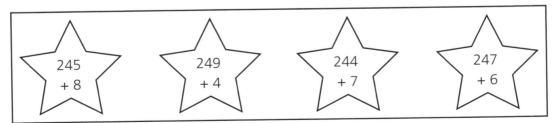

| 245 + 8 | 249 + 4 | 244 + 7 | 247 + 6 |

5. Two numbers total 105. One of the numbers is 95.

What is the other number? _____

Subtraction

Learn and revise

Break numbers up so that you can subtract them in your head.

Example: What is 136 subtract 7?

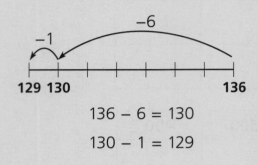

$$136 - 6 = 130$$
$$130 - 1 = 129$$

Subtract back to the next ten and then count back.

Example: Take away 30 from 155.

$$\mathbf{155} - 30 =$$
$$\mathbf{150} + \mathbf{5} - 30 =$$

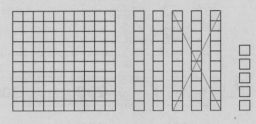

$$\underline{150 - 30 = 120} + \mathbf{5} = 125$$

Subtract the hundreds and tens and then add on the ones.

Practice activities

1. Subtract back to the next ten and then count back.

   a) $148 - 9 = \underline{}$ b) $125 - 8 = \underline{}$

   c) $163 - 6 = \underline{}$ d) $171 - 5 = \underline{}$

   e) $182 - 7 = \underline{}$ f) $198 - 9 = \underline{}$

2. Break up the numbers and then subtract carefully.

   a) $145 - 20 = \underline{}$ b) $138 - 30 = \underline{}$

   c) $179 - 50 = \underline{}$ d) $165 - 40 = \underline{}$

   e) $192 - 40 = \underline{}$ f) $154 - 50 = \underline{}$

3. Complete each chart to show the numbers coming out of each subtraction machine.

a)

IN → −60 → OUT

IN	140	170	120	110	150	130
OUT	80					

b)

IN → −200 → OUT

IN	410	465	372	845	503	283
OUT	210					

4. Answer these.

a) Take 30 away from 74. _____

b) Subtract 60 from 130. _____

c) What is 300 less than 455? _____

d) Take away 9 from 160. _____

e) What is 186 take away 50? _____

5. Write the difference between each pair of numbers.

a) | 130 | 200 | _____

b) | 190 | 50 | _____

c) | 140 | 90 | _____

d) | 70 | 160 | _____

e) | 80 | 190 | _____

f) | 170 | 80 | _____

1. Write the addition fact this shows.

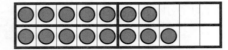

   _____ + _____ = _____

2. **9 + 4 = 13**

   Use this addition fact to answer these.

   4 + 9 = _____

   13 – 9 = _____

   13 – 4 = _____

3. Write the missing number.

   15 – _____ = 6

4. Use the number line to answer this.

   14 – 8 = _____

5. Circle the odd one out.

   12 – 5   13 – 7   11 – 4   16 – 9

6. Write the missing number.

   _____ + 5 = 18

7. Two numbers have a difference of 30. One of the numbers is 52. What could the other number be?

   _____ or _____

8. Add this mentally.

   65 + 4 = _____

9. Take 8 away from 120. _____

10. 80 + 30 = _____

11. 228 + 60 = _____

12. Add 40 to 115. _____

13. Complete this addition grid.

+	208	412	597
300	508		

14. Circle the odd one out.

   650 + 8   608 + 50   618 + 40   680 + 5

15. Use the double to help answer these.

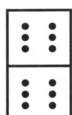

   6 + 6 = _____

   6 + 5 = _____

   6 + 7 = _____

16. 132 – 3 = _____

17. 156 – 30 = _____

18. Complete the chart to show the numbers coming out of this subtraction machine.

IN	766	504	829
OUT	466		

19. Add this mentally.

   316 + 7 = _____

20. Circle two numbers with a difference of 70.

   60   120   80   40

   150   140   90   170

Score   /20

1. 336 + 60 = _____

2. 542 – 40 = _____

3. Complete this addition grid.

+	48	99	54
7	55		

4. What number is 300 more than 654?

_____

5. Two numbers have a difference of 20. One of the numbers is 78. What could the other number be?

_____ or _____

6. What is the total of 483 and 400?

_____

7. Complete the chart to show the numbers coming out of this subtraction machine.

IN	161	56	117
OUT	153		

8. Write the missing number.

110 – _____ = 60

9. Circle the odd one out.

79 – 3   72 – 5

    73 – 6   71 – 4

10. Add this mentally.

182 + 9 = _____

11. Write the missing number.

_____ + 80 = 94

12. Write the addition fact this shows.

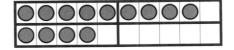

_____ + _____ = _____

13. 645 – 200 = _____

14. Join pairs of numbers with a difference of 50.

90

60   110

                130

40   80

15. Subtract 30 from 78. _____

16. Use the number line to answer this.

6   14

14 – 6 = _____

17. What number is 200 less than 608? _____

18. 259 – 40 = _____

19. Circle the odd one out.

213 + 7   190 + 30

217 + 5   170 + 50

20. I am thinking of a number. If I added 50 to the number, it would make 380. What number am I thinking of?

_____

Score   /20

19

Multiplication facts

Learn and revise

Look at these multiplication facts:

The 3 times table has an interesting pattern. The digits in the product always add up to 3, 6 or 9.

3 × 1 = 3	3 × 7 = 21
3 × 2 = 6	3 × 8 = 24
3 × 3 = 9	3 × 9 = 27
3 × 4 = 12	3 × 10 = 30
3 × 5 = 15	3 × 11 = 33
3 × 6 = 18	3 × 12 = 36

The 8 times table is double the 4 times table. The product is always an even number.

8 × 1 = 8	8 × 7 = 56
8 × 2 = 16	8 × 8 = 64
8 × 3 = 24	8 × 9 = 72
8 × 4 = 32	8 × 10 = 80
8 × 5 = 40	8 × 11 = 88
8 × 6 = 48	8 × 12 = 96

Practice activities

1. Write the answers to these.

a) ☆☆☆☆☆☆
☆☆☆☆☆☆
☆☆☆☆☆☆

6 × 3 = _____   3 × 6 = _____

b) ☆☆☆☆☆☆☆☆
☆☆☆☆☆☆☆☆
☆☆☆☆☆☆☆☆
☆☆☆☆☆☆☆☆

8 × 4 = _____   4 × 8 = _____

c) ☆☆☆☆☆☆
☆☆☆☆☆☆
☆☆☆☆☆☆
☆☆☆☆☆☆
☆☆☆☆☆☆
☆☆☆☆☆☆
☆☆☆☆☆☆
☆☆☆☆☆☆

6 × 8 = _____   8 × 6 = _____

d) ☆☆☆☆☆
☆☆☆☆☆
☆☆☆☆☆
☆☆☆☆☆
☆☆☆☆☆
☆☆☆☆☆
☆☆☆☆☆
☆☆☆☆☆

5 × 8 = _____   8 × 5 = _____

e) ☆☆☆☆☆☆☆☆☆
☆☆☆☆☆☆☆☆☆
☆☆☆☆☆☆☆☆☆

9 × 3 = _____   3 × 9 = _____

f) ☆☆☆☆☆☆☆☆☆☆☆
☆☆☆☆☆☆☆☆☆☆☆
☆☆☆☆☆☆☆☆☆☆☆

3 × 11 = _____   11 × 3 = _____

2. Write four different facts for each number. Use the beads to help you.

a) ____ × ____   ____ × ____

24

____ × ____   ____ × ____

b) ____ × ____   ____ × ____

48

____ × ____   ____ × ____

c) ____ × ____   ____ × ____

36

____ × ____   ____ × ____

3. Use doubling to answer these.

a) $5 \times 2 = 10$

$5 \times 4 = 20$

$5 \times 8 =$ ____

b) $7 \times 2 =$ ____

$7 \times 4 =$ ____

$7 \times 8 =$ ____

c) $4 \times 2 =$ ____

$4 \times 4 =$ ____

$4 \times 8 =$ ____

d) $6 \times 2 =$ ____

$6 \times 4 =$ ____

$6 \times 8 =$ ____

e) $12 \times 2 =$ ____

$12 \times 4 =$ ____

$12 \times 8 =$ ____

f) $9 \times 2 =$ ____

$9 \times 4 =$ ____

$9 \times 8 =$ ____

4. Complete these. Circle those you know instantly.

$8 \times 2 =$ ____ $4 \times 10 =$ ____ $5 \times 9 =$ ____ $7 \times 3 =$ ____

$3 \times 6 =$ ____ $9 \times 2 =$ ____ $8 \times 4 =$ ____ $10 \times 7 =$ ____

$7 \times 8 =$ ____ $3 \times 2 =$ ____ $9 \times 3 =$ ____ $6 \times 6 =$ ____

$9 \times 5 =$ ____ $8 \times 3 =$ ____ $4 \times 9 =$ ____ $6 \times 4 =$ ____

Multiplication

Use the tables facts that you know to help you multiply bigger numbers.

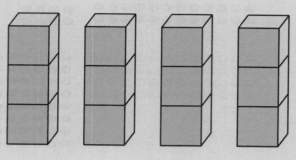

3 × 4 = 12

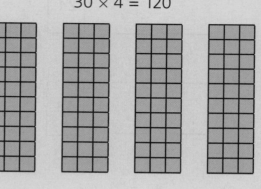

30 × 4 = 120

Practice activities

1. Answer these.

   a) 4 × 5 = ____

      40 × 5 = ____

   b) 3 × 8 = ____

      30 × 8 = ____

   c) 6 × 4 = ____

      60 × 4 = ____

   d) 9 × 2 = ____

      90 × 2 = ____

   e) 5 × 5 = ____

      50 × 5 = ____

   f) 3 × 7 = ____

      30 × 7 = ____

2. Complete these multiplication grids.

   a)

×	20	50	80
3	60		
6			
4			

   b)

×	3	5	4
60			
30			
90			

3. Colour the odd one out in each set.

a)

40 × 2 20 × 4 30 × 3 10 × 8

b)

40 × 6 60 × 4 30 × 8 50 × 5

c)

90 × 4 60 × 6 40 × 9 80 × 5

4. The two base numbers on each triangle are multiplied to give the top number. Write the missing numbers on these triangles.

a)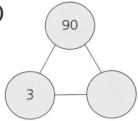

90
3

b)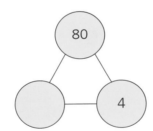

80
4

c)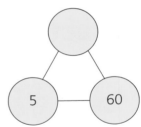

5 60

d)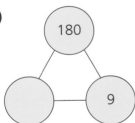

180
9

e)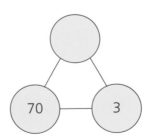

70 3

f)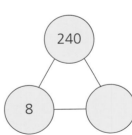

240
8

5. Multiply these sets of three numbers. Look for pairs to multiply first.

Example:

$3 \times 5 \times 4 = 3 \times 20 = 60$

5 4

a)

2
6 5

b)

10
4 6

c)

5
8 3

d)

2
9 5

_____ _____ _____ _____

Division

Learn and revise

Look at these divisions:

Here are 18 counters divided into 3s.

This shows that there are 6 groups.

$$18 \div 3 = 6$$

Here are 22 counters divided into 4s.

This shows that there are 5 groups with 2 counters left over.

$$22 \div 4 = 5 \text{ remainder } 2$$

Practice activities

1. Group these and write the answer.

   a) ☆☆☆☆☆☆☆☆
      ☆☆☆☆☆☆☆☆
      ☆☆☆☆☆☆☆☆

      $24 \div 3 =$ ____

   b) ☆☆☆☆☆☆☆
      ☆☆☆☆☆☆☆
      ☆☆☆☆☆☆☆
      ☆☆☆☆☆☆☆

      $28 \div 4 =$ ____

   c) ☆☆☆☆☆☆☆☆☆
      ☆☆☆☆☆☆☆☆☆
      ☆☆☆☆☆☆☆☆☆

      $27 \div 3 =$ ____

   d) ☆☆☆☆☆☆☆☆☆☆☆☆
      ☆☆☆☆☆☆☆☆☆☆☆☆
      ☆☆☆☆☆☆☆☆☆☆☆☆

      $36 \div 3 =$ ____

   e) ☆☆☆☆☆☆☆☆☆☆☆
      ☆☆☆☆☆☆☆☆☆☆☆
      ☆☆☆☆☆☆☆☆☆☆☆
      ☆☆☆☆☆☆☆☆☆☆☆

      $44 \div 4 =$ ____

   f) ☆☆☆☆☆☆☆☆
      ☆☆☆☆☆☆☆☆
      ☆☆☆☆☆☆☆☆
      ☆☆☆☆☆☆☆☆

      $32 \div 4 =$ ____

2. Complete each chart to show the numbers coming out of each division machine.

a)

IN → ÷5 → OUT

IN	30	50	80	100	70	60
OUT	6					

b)

IN → ÷10 → OUT

IN	90	120	150	200	180	170
OUT	9					

3. Divide these and join each division to the matching remainder.

28 ÷ 3

no remainder
1
2
3
4
5

36 ÷ 2

42 ÷ 5

39 ÷ 5

43 ÷ 4

55 ÷ 10

4. Divide these and write the answers.

a)

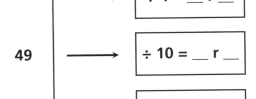

49 → ÷ 4 = __ r __
   → ÷ 10 = __ r __
   → ÷ 2 = __ r __

b)

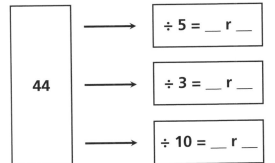

44 → ÷ 5 = __ r __
   → ÷ 3 = __ r __
   → ÷ 10 = __ r __

Mental arithmetic test 5

1. Write the multiplication fact shown.

_____ × _____ = 18

2. 9 × 5 = _____

3. 30 ÷ 6 = _____

4. Underline the numbers that divide exactly into 24.

  2   4   6   8

     3   5   7   9

5. Write the answers for these.

8 × 2 = _____

8 × 4 = _____

8 × 8 = _____

6. 160 ÷ 10 = _____

7. 40 × 5 = _____

8. 90 ÷ 5 = _____

9. Join pairs of multiplications with the same answer.

9 × 4

      3 × 8

               6 × 6

8 × 2

   4 × 4

       4 × 6

10. What is the remainder when 30 is divided by 4?

r = _____

11. 20 × 8 = _____

12. Circle the odd one out.

42 ÷ 7

                       48 ÷ 8

           54 ÷ 9

    56 ÷ 7

13. 5 × 7 × 2 = _____

14. 250 ÷ 5 = _____

15. Multiply 60 by 5. _____

16. Circle the two divisions with a remainder of 4.

              49 ÷ 6

38 ÷ 5   25 ÷ 7

                   54 ÷ 9

      20 ÷ 8

17. 56 ÷ 7 = _____

18. A box holds 40 apples. How many apples are there in nine boxes?

_____

19. 43 ÷ 8 = _____ r _____

20. Answer these.

7 × 7 = _____

7 × 70 = _____

1. 4 × 8 = _____

2. Answer these.

   7 × 2 = _____

   7 × 4 = _____

   7 × 8 = _____

3. 30 ÷ 6 = _____

4. 9 × 9 = _____

5. What is the remainder when 3 is divided into 29?

   r = _____

6. Circle the number that **cannot** be divided exactly by 5.

   35   90   54   45

   15   70   20

7. Circle the odd one out.

   5 × 12

   2 × 30   4 × 30

   6 × 10   3 × 20

8. 27 ÷ 3 = _____

9. 65 ÷ 8 = _____ r _____

10. What is the answer when 3 is multiplied by itself?

    _____

11. Answer these.

    4 × 6 = _____

    4 × 60 = _____

12. Divide 72 by 8. _____

13. 9 × 6 = _____

14. 50 × 3 = _____

15. 80 × 7 = _____

16. Join pairs of divisions with the same remainder.

    45 ÷ 6   13 ÷ 3

    20 ÷ 9   17 ÷ 4

    58 ÷ 8   31 ÷ 7

17. 3 × 6 × 4 = _____

18. 63 ÷ 9 = _____

19. This machine divides by 10. Complete the chart.

IN	80	100	130
OUT	8		

20. 2 × 9 × 5 = _____

Score /20

27

Addition and subtraction problems

Learn and revise

Look out for addition and subtraction words in any problems. They can give a clue for how to solve the problem.

Addition words	Subtraction words
add, total, altogether, sum, plus, more than, increase	subtract, take away, minus, less than, fewer, difference, reduce

Be careful. Some problems can be confusing. Read them carefully and 'picture' the problem.

Example: Two mobile phones have a difference in price of £30. The more expensive one costs £120. How much is the cheaper one?

£120 − £30 = £90

Practice activities

1. **a)** A loaf of bread costs 80p. It is reduced in price by 15p.

    What is the cost of the loaf now? _____ p

    b) There are 200 children in Sam's school and 190 children in Joel's school.

    How many children are there in total in the two schools? _____

    c) A lorry travels 35 km to collect boxes of vegetables from a farm and 60 km to the town market.

    How far did the lorry travel altogether? _____ km

    d) Becky scored 145 points on a computer game. Hannah scored 8 fewer points than Becky.

    How many points did Hannah score? _____

    e) Dan buys shoes for £28 and a coat for £40.

    How much does he spend altogether? £ _____

    f) The difference in length between two sticks is 12 cm.

    If the longer stick is 50 cm, how long is the shorter stick? _____ cm

Addition and subtraction problems

2. This chart shows the number of balls made in a factory over three days.

   a) Complete the totals.

	Footballs	Basketballs	Tennis balls	Total number of balls
Monday	40	60	100	
Tuesday	70	50	120	
Wednesday	60	50	80	
Total of each ball				

   b) How many more tennis balls than basketballs were made in total? _____

   c) How many fewer balls were made on Monday than on Tuesday? _____

3. Look at the map and answer these questions.

   a) On Tuesday the doctor drives from the town to the village and then on to the school. How far does the doctor travel? _____ miles

   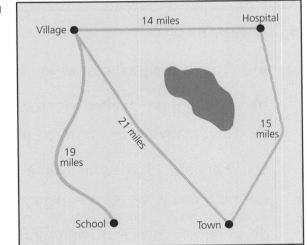

   b) A bus goes from the town to the hospital and then to the village. How far does the bus travel on this journey in total? _____ miles

   c) How much further is it from the town to the village than from the hospital to the village? _____ miles

   d) On Wednesday the doctor travels from the hospital to the village and then drives on to the school. How far does he travel altogether? _____ miles

   e) How much further is it from the school to the village than from the hospital to the village? _____ miles

Multiplication and division problems

Learn and revise

Look out for multiplication and division words in any problems. They can give a clue for how to solve the problem.

Multiplication words	Division words
multiply, times, product, groups of, sets of	divide, group, share, fraction, remainder

Always look carefully to see if your answer makes sense. When you divide and there is a remainder, check to see if the answer should be rounded up or down.

Example: Oranges are put in bags, with six oranges fitting in each bag. How many bags are needed for 20 oranges?

$20 \div 6 = 3$ remainder 2

This means that four bags are needed to hold all the oranges.

Practice activities

1. Answer these.

    a) What is the total cost of four lamps each costing £30? £ _____

    b) Six beans are planted in a row. There are 20 beans in a packet.
    How many full rows can be planted from this pack of beans? _____

    c) There are 25 jelly sweets in a bag.
    How many sweets are there in four bags? _____

    d) A farmer collects 40 eggs and puts them into egg boxes that hold 12 eggs. All the eggs must be in an egg box.
    How many egg boxes will he need? _____

    e) A cushion costs £7. What is the total price for four cushions? £ _____

    f) A ribbon is 85 cm in length.
    How many 10 cm lengths can be made from this ribbon? _____

Answers

Pages 4–5
1. **a)** 95, 96, 99 **b)** 109, 112, 113
   c) 379, 380, 383 **d)** 706, 707, 708
   e) 598, 599, 600
2. **a)** 32 **b)** 170 **c)** 52 **d)** 400 **e)** 48
3. **a)** 30, 33, 45, 48 **b)** 40, 50, 90, 100
   c) 28, 32, 48, 52 **d)** 8, 16, 48, 56
4. 170, 200, 230
   660, 690, 730
5. **a)** 710, 810, 910 **b)** 600, 610, 620
   c) 645, 745, 845 **d)** 284, 294, 304
6. No
7. 25

Pages 6–7
1. **a)** 80 **b)** 600
   c) 50, 4 **d)** 700, 90
   e) 100, 8
2. **a)** 638 **b)** 417 **c)** 780 **d)** 503
3. **a)** 437 **b)** 694 **c)** 918 **d)** 189
4. **a)** 725 **b)** 478 **c)** 303 **d)** 427
5. **a)** 413 **b)** 625 **c)** 704
6. **a)** 58 → 30 + 28, 20 + 38, 10 + 48
   b) 63 → 50 + 13, 40 + 23, 30 + 33, 20 + 43, 10 + 53
   c) 47 → 40 + 7, 30 + 17, 20 + 27, 10 + 37

Pages 8–9
1. **a)** < **b)** > **c)** > **d)** <
2. 238, (573)
3. **a)** 258, 285, 302, 311 **b)** 509, 568, 589, 600
   c) 677, 721, 729, 784 **d)** 467, 476, 647, 674
4. **a)** Any number between 38 and 54
   b) Any number between 93 and 106
   c) Any number between 245 and 290
   d) 513 or 514
5. Rivers should be listed in this order: River Severn – 354 km;
   River Thames – 346 km; River Trent – 297 km; River Wye –
   215 km; River Tay – 188 km; River Clyde – 172 km

Page 10
1. 290 **2.** 863
3. 140, 143 **4.** 80
5. 508
6. 586 g, 589 g, 590 g, 658 g, 685 g
7. 600, 90 **8.** 700
9. 54, 60 **10.** <
11. 253, 325, 352, 523, 532 **12.** 983
13. Any one of: 219, 220, 221, 222, 223, 224, 225
14. 407 **15.** 681
16. No **17.** 100, 250
18. 842 **19.** Six hundred and eighteen
20. 16, 24, 56, 64

Page 11
1. 507 **2.** 452, 453, 456
3. 300, 10 **4.** 754
5. 385 cm, 358 cm, 299 cm, 285 cm, 258 cm
6. >
7. Three hundred and eighty-nine
8. 247 **9.** 512 km
10. 40
11.

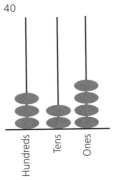

12. 725, 825 **13.** 406
14. Any one of: 298, 299, 300
15. 32, 36, 52, 56 **16.** 30, 8, 638
17. 408 **18.** 450
19. 909, 911, 912, 921, 935 **20.** 560

Pages 12–13
1. **a)** 7 + 4 = 11 **b)** 9 + 6 = 15
   c) 5 + 8 = 13 **d)** 6 + 7 = 13
   e) 8 + 6 = 14 **f)** 7 + 7 = 14
2. **a)** 13, 7, 6 **b)** 14, 5, 9
   c) 15, 8, 7 **d)** 15, 9, 6
3. **a)** 12, 13, 11 **b)** 16, 17, 15
   c) 10, 11, 9 **d)** 14, 15, 13
   e) 18, 19, 17
4. **a)** 7 **b)** 9 **c)** 4 **d)** 6 **e)** 7 **f)** 9
5. 6 → 14 – 8, 11 – 5, 12 – 6
   7 → 13 – 6, 14 – 7, 15 – 8
   8 → 15 – 7, 12 – 4, 11 – 3
   9 → 15 – 6, 17 – 8, 13 – 4
6. **a)** 6 **b)** 4 **c)** 11 **d)** 11
   e) 6 **f)** 7 **g)** 12 **h)** 13

Pages 14–15
1. **a)** 88 **b)** 33 **c)** 62 **d)** 96
   e) 145 **f)** 235 **g)** 241 **h)** 357
2. **a)** 81 **b)** 94 **c)** 93 **d)** 91
   e) 274 **f)** 177 **g)** 291 **h)** 389
3. **a)**

+	30	60	20	50
134	164	194	154	184
211	241	271	231	261
302	332	362	322	352

   b)

+	200	300	500	400
123	323	423	623	523
307	507	607	807	707
528	728	828	1028	928

4. **a)** 350 + 20 **b)** 50 + 55 **c)** 244 + 7
5. 10

Pages 16–17
1. **a)** 139 **b)** 117 **c)** 157 **d)** 166 **e)** 175 **f)** 189
2. **a)** 125 **b)** 108 **c)** 129 **d)** 125 **e)** 152 **f)** 104
3. **a)** Bottom row should be completed as follows:
   110, 60, 50, 90, 70
   b) Bottom row should be completed as follows:
   265, 172, 645, 303, 83
4. **a)** 44 **b)** 70 **c)** 155 **d)** 151 **e)** 136
5. **a)** 70 **b)** 140 **c)** 50 **d)** 90 **e)** 110 **f)** 90

Page 18
1. 7 + 8 = 15 **2.** 13, 4, 9 **3.** 9
4. 6 **5.** 13 – 7 **6.** 13
7. 22 or 82 **8.** 69 **9.** 112
10. 110 **11.** 288 **12.** 155
13. 712, 897 **14.** 680 + 5 **15.** 12, 11, 13
16. 129 **17.** 126 **18.** 204, 529
19. 323 **20.** 80 and 150

Page 19
1. 396 **2.** 502 **3.** 106, 61
4. 954 **5.** 58 or 98 **6.** 883
7. 48, 109 **8.** 50 **9.** 79 – 3
10. 191 **11.** 14 **12.** 9 + 4 = 13

Answers

13. 445
14. 130 and 80, 60 and 110, 90 and 40
15. 48
16. 8
17. 408
18. 219
19. 217 + 5
20. 330

Pages 20–21
1. a) 18, 18   b) 32, 32   c) 48, 48
   d) 40, 40   e) 27, 27   f) 33, 33
2. a) Any four of these: 3 × 8, 8 × 3, 6 × 4, 4 × 6, 2 × 12, 12 × 2, 1 × 24, 24 × 1
   b) Any four of these: 4 × 12, 12 × 4, 8 × 6, 6 × 8, 3 × 16, 16 × 3, 24 × 2, 2 × 24, 1 × 48, 48 × 1
   c) Any four of these: 6 × 6, 9 × 4, 4 × 9, 3 × 12, 12 × 3, 2 × 18, 18 × 2, 1 × 36, 36 × 1
3. a) 40   b) 14, 28, 56
   c) 8, 16, 32   d) 12, 24, 48
   e) 24, 48, 96   f) 18, 36, 72
4.
16	40	45	21
18	18	32	70
56	6	27	36
45	24	36	24

Pages 22–23
1. a) 20, 200   b) 24, 240
   c) 24, 240   d) 18, 180
   e) 25, 250   f) 21, 210

2. a)

×	20	50	80
3	60	150	240
6	120	300	480
4	80	200	320

   b)

×	3	5	4
60	180	300	240
30	90	150	120
90	270	450	360

3. a) 30 × 3   b) 50 × 5   c) 80 × 5
4. a) 30   b) 20   c) 300
   d) 20   e) 210   f) 30
5. a) 60   b) 240
   c) 120   d) 90

Pages 24–25
1. a) 8   b) 7   c) 9   d) 12   e) 11   f) 8
2. a) Bottom row should be completed as follows:
     10, 16, 20, 14, 12
   b) Bottom row should be completed as follows:
     12, 15, 20, 18, 17
3. no remainder → 36 ÷ 2
     1 → 28 ÷ 3
     2 → 42 ÷ 5
     3 → 43 ÷ 4
     4 → 39 ÷ 5
     5 → 55 ÷ 10
4. a) 12 r 1, 4 r 9, 24 r 1   b) 8 r 4, 14 r 2, 4 r 4

Page 26
1. 3 × 6 or 6 × 3   **2.** 45
3. 5   **4.** 2, 3, 4, 6, 8
5. 16, 32, 64   **6.** 16
7. 200   **8.** 18
9. 9 × 4 and 6 × 6; 3 × 8 and 4 × 6; 8 × 2 and 4 × 4
10. r 2   **11.** 160
12. 56 ÷ 7   **13.** 70

14. 50   **15.** 300
16. 25 ÷ 7 and 20 ÷ 8   **17.** 8
18. 360   **19.** 5 r 3   **20.** 49, 490

Page 27
1. 32   **2.** 14, 28, 56   **3.** 5
4. 81   **5.** r 2   **6.** 54
7. 4 × 30   **8.** 9   **9.** 8 r 1
10. 9   **11.** 24, 240   **12.** 9
13. 54   **14.** 150   **15.** 560
16. 13 ÷ 3 and 17 ÷ 4; 58 ÷ 8 and 20 ÷ 9; 45 ÷ 6 and 31 ÷ 7
17. 72   **18.** 7
19. 10, 13   **20.** 90

Pages 28–29
1. a) 65p   b) 390
   c) 95 km   d) 137
   e) £68   f) 38 cm
2. a)
   Monday → 200
   Tuesday → 240
   Wednesday → 190
   Footballs → 170
   Basketballs → 160
   Tennis balls → 300
   Total → 630
   b) 140   c) 40
3. a) 40 miles   b) 29 miles
   c) 7 miles   d) 33 miles
   e) 5 miles

Pages 30–31
1. a) £120   b) 3
   c) 100   d) 4
   e) £28   f) 8
2. a) Guava   b) Orange
   c) Mango   d) Melon
3. 37

Pages 32–33
1. a) 240   b) 7
   c) 120   d) 3
   e) 48   f) 12
   g) 16   h) 48

2.

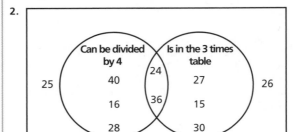

3. a) 12   b) 6   c) 4   d) 3   e) 2
4. a) 45, 25   b) 45, 60, 30   c) 45, 25
   d) 80, 30   e) 80
5. 90 g, 110 g
6. **4 × 6** = 24 (or **6 × 4** = 24), **27** ÷ 3 = 9, **3 × 5** = 15, 30 ÷ **5** = 6
7. 15

Page 34
1. 155 km   **2.** 150
3. 24   **4.** 200 m
5. 480   **6.** 32
7. 72   **8.** 63
9. 54   **10.** 30 km
11. 189   **12.** 89p

13. 30   **14.** 8
15. 124 cm   **16.** 44p
17. 23   **18.** 8
19. 6   **20.** 14 and 10

Page 35
1. 6   **2.** 2
3. 6 and 7   **4.** 240
5. 221   **6.** 56, 49
7. 78   **8.** 26
9. 48   **10.** 50
11. 144   **12.** 653
13. 553   **14.** 15
15. £36   **16.** 243 g
17. 150 g   **18.** 133 kg
19. 3   **20.** £125

Pages 36–37
1. a) $\frac{3}{4}$ b) $\frac{1}{6}$ c) $\frac{5}{8}$ d) $\frac{2}{5}$
2. a) $\frac{1}{3}, \frac{2}{6}$ b) $\frac{3}{4}, \frac{9}{12}$ c) $\frac{1}{2}, \frac{5}{10}$ d) $\frac{2}{5}, \frac{4}{10}$
3. a) $\frac{1}{2} = \frac{2}{4} = \frac{3}{6} = \frac{4}{8} = \frac{5}{10} = \frac{6}{12}$
   b) $\frac{1}{3} = \frac{2}{6} = \frac{3}{9} = \frac{4}{12} = \frac{5}{15} = \frac{6}{18}$
   c) $\frac{1}{4} = \frac{2}{8} = \frac{3}{12} = \frac{4}{16} = \frac{5}{20} = \frac{6}{24}$
   d) $\frac{1}{5} = \frac{2}{10} = \frac{3}{15} = \frac{4}{20} = \frac{5}{25} = \frac{6}{30}$

Pages 38–39
1. a) 3   b) 2
   c) 5   d) 4
2. a) 7   b) 10
   c) 7   d) 5
   e) 7   f) 11
3. $\frac{1}{5}$ of 20 = 4, $\frac{1}{2}$ of 20 = 10, $\frac{1}{4}$ of 20 = 5, so $\frac{1}{2}$
4. True
5. a) <   b) >
   c) >   d) >
   e) <   f) >
6. 12 chickens, 6 goats, 4 cows, 2 ducks

Pages 40–41
1. a) $\frac{4}{10}$, 0.4   b) $\frac{9}{10}$, 0.9
   c) $1\frac{2}{10}$, 1.2   d) $1\frac{5}{10}$, 1.5
   e) $2\frac{1}{10}$, 2.1   f) $2\frac{7}{10}$, 2.7
2. a) $\frac{2}{4}$ (or $\frac{1}{2}$)   b) $\frac{2}{6}$ (or $\frac{1}{3}$)
   c) $\frac{4}{10}$ (or $\frac{2}{5}$)   d) $\frac{4}{5}$
3. All answers equal 1.
   a) $\frac{3}{3}$ or 1   b) $\frac{4}{4}$ or 1
   c) $\frac{2}{2}$ or 1   d) $\frac{5}{5}$ or 1
4. $\frac{1}{6}, \frac{1}{4}, \frac{1}{3}, \frac{1}{2}, \frac{2}{3}, \frac{3}{4}$

Page 42
1. $\frac{3}{8}$ **2.** Any two parts shaded
3. $\frac{2}{4}$ **4.** $\frac{4}{12}$
5. 5   **6.** <
7. 0.3   **8.** $\frac{5}{9}$
9. $\frac{2}{12}$ **10.** Any two parts shaded
11. $\frac{4}{10}$, 0.4   **12.** $\frac{1}{6}, \frac{1}{4}, \frac{1}{3}, \frac{1}{2}$
13. $\frac{4}{5}$ **14.** True
15. $\frac{2}{10}, \frac{3}{15}$ **16.** 5
17. 18   **18.** 12
19. 6   **20.** 9

Page 43
1. Any six parts shaded   **2.** 9
3. $\frac{4}{8}$ **4.** $\frac{2}{6}$ or $\frac{1}{3}$
5. $\frac{4}{7}$ **6.** $1\frac{8}{10}$, 1.8
7. 10   **8.** 15
9. 5   **10.** 6
11. 0.7   **12.** False
13. $\frac{8}{10}$ (or $\frac{4}{5}$)   **14.** >
15. $\frac{1}{4}$ **16.** $\frac{1}{10}, \frac{1}{5}, \frac{1}{4}, \frac{1}{2}$
17. 4   **18.** $\frac{6}{10}$ (or $\frac{3}{5}$)
19. $\frac{1}{3}$ of 24   **20.** $\frac{2}{20}, \frac{3}{30}$

Pages 44–45
1. 1 m 25 cm → 125 cm
   1 m 20 cm → 120 cm
   120 mm → 12 cm
   3 m → 300 cm
   300 mm → 30 cm
   3 cm → 30 mm
2. a) >   b) =
   c) >   d) <
   e) >   f) =
3. a) 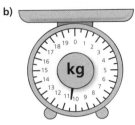   b)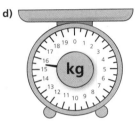
   c) 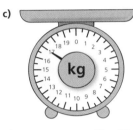   d)
4. a) 5   b) 20
   c) 4   d) 20
   e) 4
5. Three 50 cm and two 90 cm length pipes

Pages 46–47
1. a) 97p   b) 79p   c) 71p
2. a) Two 20p and two 5p coins or one 20p and three 10p coins
   b) One 10p and one 50p coins
   c) One 50p, one 10p, two 2p and one 1p coins or two 20p, two 10p and one 5p coins
3. a) 50p, 20p, 10p, 5p coins
   b) £1, 20p, 2p, 2p coins
   c) 50p, 20p, 20p, 5p, 2p, 2p coins
4. 20p
5. a) £4   b) £3
   c) £2   d) £6
6. a) £12   b) £36
   c) £45   d) £18
   e) 8

Pages 48–49
1. a) 3:10   b) 4:25
   c) 9:35   d) 11:30
   e) 1:40   f) 2:20
   g) 10:15   h) 5:05
2. a)   b)   c)
   afternoon   morning   morning
   d)    e)   f)
   morning   afternoon   evening

Answers

3. a) 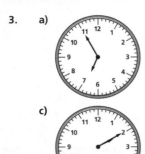 b)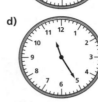

c) d)

4. a) 2 minutes   b) 21 days
     c) 240 minutes   d) 2 weeks
     e) 150 seconds   f) 90 minutes
     g) 48 months   h) 10 hours

Page 50
1. 4   **2.** £1.20
3. 6   **4.** £1.10
5. £2   **6.** 90p
7.

8. 50p, 20p, 20p, 5p
9. 1500 g   **10.** 7 kg, $3\frac{1}{2}$ kg
11. 450 cm   **12.** =, <
13. 10p, 10p, 5p
14. 10:20, 4:35   **15.** 400 cm
16. 29p
17.

18. 2 weeks
19.

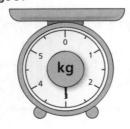

20. 18 cm

Page 51
1.

2. evening, morning   **3.** 5
4. 350 cm   **5.** 24 months
6. 10p, 2p, 2p, 1p   **7.** 20
8. 1:50
9.

10. 5   **11.** 600 minutes
12. 11.10 a.m.   **13.** 4 cm
14. 52p   **15.** 3 minutes
16. £25   **17.** £14
18. £3   **19.** 20p, 20p, 10p
20. <, =

Page 52

1.	9	**2.**	4	**3.**	7	**4.**	3
5.	6	**6.**	1	**7.**	8	**8.**	9
9.	9	**10.**	5	**11.**	15	**12.**	19
13.	11	**14.**	20	**15.**	15	**16.**	14
17.	14	**18.**	18	**19.**	14	**20.**	12
21.	11	**22.**	16	**23.**	12	**24.**	4
25.	8	**26.**	11	**27.**	7	**28.**	15
29.	9	**30.**	8	**31.**	13	**32.**	12
33.	6	**34.**	7	**35.**	11	**36.**	6
37.	14	**38.**	13	**39.**	10	**40.**	13

Page 54

1.	18	**2.**	32	**3.**	18	**4.**	7
5.	64	**6.**	6	**7.**	9	**8.**	8
9.	80	**10.**	24	**11.**	14	**12.**	24
13.	5	**14.**	36	**15.**	210	**16.**	5
17.	16	**18.**	10	**19.**	16	**20.**	5
21.	6	**22.**	48	**23.**	45	**24.**	7
25.	10	**26.**	6	**27.**	9	**28.**	4
29.	90	**30.**	12	**31.**	8	**32.**	5
33.	7	**34.**	36	**35.**	7	**36.**	200
37.	160	**38.**	54	**39.**	5	**40.**	60

Page 56

1.	30	**2.**	12	**3.**	17	**4.**	28
5.	4	**6.**	30	**7.**	27	**8.**	14
9.	7	**10.**	5	**11.**	5	**12.**	24
13.	2	**14.**	36	**15.**	10	**16.**	6
17.	160	**18.**	17	**19.**	7	**20.**	11
21.	13	**22.**	5	**23.**	6	**24.**	11
25.	17	**26.**	9	**27.**	12	**28.**	25
29.	80	**30.**	15	**31.**	13	**32.**	5
33.	7	**34.**	8	**35.**	14	**36.**	6
37.	11	**38.**	40	**39.**	14	**40.**	24

Published by Letts Educational
An imprint of HarperCollins*Publishers*
77–85 Fulham Palace Road
London W6 8JB

ISBN 9781844197309

Text © 2013 Paul Broadbent

Design © 2013 Letts Educational, an imprint of HarperCollins*Publishers*

The author asserts his moral right to be identified as the author of this work.

All rights reserved. No part of this publication may be reproduced, stored in a retrieval system, or transmitted, in any form or by any means, electronic, mechanical, photocopying, recording or otherwise, without the prior permission of Letts Educational.

Multiplication and division problems

2. Answer these multiplications and divisions and write the matching code letter shown in the chart. Find the names of four fruits.

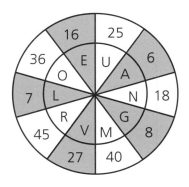

a) 2 × 4 = __8__ __G__

    5 × 5 = ____ ____

    24 ÷ 4 = ____ ____

    3 × 9 = ____ ____

    48 ÷ 8 = ____ ____

b) 6 × 6 = ____ ____

    9 × 5 = ____ ____

    18 ÷ 3 = ____ ____

    3 × 6 = ____ ____

    32 ÷ 4 = ____ ____

    2 × 8 = ____ ____

c) 4 × 10 = ____ ____

    54 ÷ 9 = ____ ____

    9 × 2 = ____ ____

    24 ÷ 3 = ____ ____

    4 × 9 = ____ ____

d) 5 × 8 = ____ ____

    4 × 4 = ____ ____

    49 ÷ 7 = ____ ____

    3 × 12 = ____ ____

    9 × 2 = ____ ____

3. James has a box of shells collected from the beach. He knows he has between 30 and 40 shells but groups them to count them. He puts them into groups of three and has one shell left over. He tries again, putting them in groups of four this time, but he still has one left over.

How many shells does he have? ____

Mixed problems

Learn and revise

Read each problem, diagram or puzzle carefully. Draw pictures or use objects to help if you are struggling to work it out in your head.

Practice activities

1. Read and answer these.

   a) What is 40 multiplied by 6? _____

   b) How much more is 32 than 25? _____

   c) What number is 10 times greater than 12? _____

   d) What is the difference between 99 and 102? _____

   e) What is 12 multiplied by 4? _____

   f) What is 36 divided by 3? _____

   g) What number is 9 less than 25? _____

   h) What number when divided by 2 gives an answer of 24? _____

2. Write these numbers in the correct part of this Venn diagram.

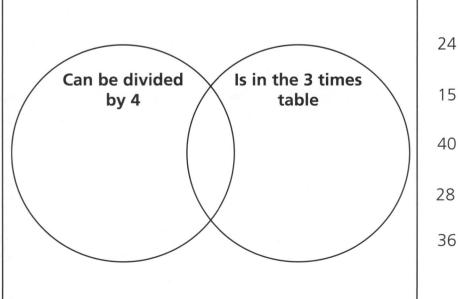

3. Look at this clock face. There are 60 minutes in one hour. Answer these questions.

a) How many groups of 5 minutes are there in one hour? _____

b) How many groups of 10 minutes are there in one hour? _____

c) How many groups of 15 minutes are there in one hour? _____

d) How many groups of 20 minutes are there in one hour? _____

e) How many groups of 30 minutes are there in one hour? _____

4. Choose numbers from the five leaves to answer each question.

a) Which two numbers leave a remainder of 1 when divided by 2?

_____ and _____

b) Which three numbers divide exactly by 3?

_____, _____ and _____

c) Which two numbers total 70? _____ and _____

d) Which two numbers have a difference of 50? _____ and _____

e) Which number is $4 \times 4 \times 5$? _____

5. Two necklaces have a difference in weight of 20 g. When they are put together they have a total weight of 200 g. What is the weight of each necklace?

_____g and _____g

6. Find a place for each of the digits 1–6.

$\boxed{} \times \boxed{} = 24$ $\boxed{}7 \div 3 = 9$ $\boxed{} \times 5 = \boxed{}5$ $30 \div \boxed{} = 6$

7. Ali is making filled rolls in his sandwich shop. He has three different types of rolls and five different types of fillings.

How many different filled rolls can he sell? _____

Mental arithmetic test 7

1. A lorry travels 85 km in the morning and 70 km in the afternoon. How far did the lorry travel altogether?

   _____ km

2. A teacher gives a daily tables test. There are 30 questions in each test. How many questions are there in total over five days?

   _____

3. There are 19 people on a bus. At a bus stop seven people get on the bus and two get off the bus. How many people are on the bus now?

   _____

4. A swimming pool is 50 m long. Jess swims four lengths. How many metres does she swim in total?

   _____

5. A book has 540 pages and I have read 60 pages. How many more pages will I need to read to finish the book?

   _____

   Look at these numbers for 6–9.

   63   32   40   9

6. Which number leaves a remainder of 2 when divided by 5?

   _____

7. Add together the two even numbers.

   _____

8. Which number is $3 \times 7 \times 3$? _____

9. What is the difference between the two odd numbers?

   _____

10. Alice travels 3 km to school and another 3 km home from school. She goes to school five days a week. How far does she travel in total in one week?

    _____ km

11. There are 196 children in a school. Today seven are absent. How many children are in school today?

    _____

12. What is the total of 83p and 6p?

    _____ p

13. There are five pairs of socks in a pack and two single socks in each pair. How many single socks are there in three packs?

    _____

14. 48 flowers are shared equally between six vases. How many are in each vase?

    _____

15. Jo is 50 cm shorter than her mum. Her mum is 174 cm tall. How tall is Jo?

    _____ cm

16. What is the total cost of a 30p ruler and a 14p pencil?

    _____ p

17. A brown chicken laid 28 eggs in a month. A white chicken laid five fewer eggs than the brown chicken. How many eggs did the white chicken lay?

    _____

    Here are 24 beads. Now answer 18–20.

18. All the beads are used to make three necklaces each with the same number of beads. How many are on each necklace?

    _____

19. There are four different colour beads: red, blue, green, yellow. There is the same number of beads of each colour. How many red beads will there be?

    _____

20. Two necklaces are made using all the beads. One necklace has four more beads than the other. How many beads are there on each necklace?

    _____ and _____

Score   /20

34

Thirty children are placed into teams. Now answer 1–2.

1. If they are placed in teams of five players for basketball, how many basketball teams will there be?

   _____

2. If they are placed in teams of seven players for netball, how many children will **not** be in a team?

   _____

3. The sum of two numbers is 13. The difference between the two numbers is 1. What are the two numbers?

   _____ and _____

4. A box has 40 nails. How many nails will there be in six boxes?

   _____

5. Sam had read 212 pages of his book and today read another 9 pages. How many pages has he read altogether?

   _____

Look at these numbers for 6–9.

       56   48   30   49

6. Which numbers divide exactly by 7?

   _____ and _____

7. What is the smallest total that can be made from adding **two** of the numbers?

   _____

8. What is the difference between the smallest and largest number?

   _____

9. Which number is $6 \times 4 \times 2$? _____

10. There are 100 pencils in a box. A teacher takes 30 to use in class and 20 are taken out as they are broken. How many pencils are left in the box?

    _____

These are the numbers of visitors to a zoo over a weekend. Use them in 11–13.

	Sat	Sun
Adults	300	353
Children	344	200

11. How many more children visited the zoo on Saturday than Sunday?

    _____

12. How many adults visited the zoo in total over the two days?

    _____

13. How many visitors were there altogether on Sunday?

    _____

14. A 5-litre bucket is used to fill a 75-litre pond. How many buckets of water will be needed to fill this pond?

    _____

15. A chair costs £9. How much will four chairs cost?

    £ _____

16. What is 250 g minus 7 g? _____ g

17. What is the total weight of five apples each weighing 30 g?

    _____ g

18. What is 8 kg more than 125 kg?

    _____ kg

19. A group of eight children equally share a pack of 24 balloons. How many balloons will they each have?

    _____

20. A bike costs £145. In a sale it is reduced by £20. How much will the bike cost now?

    £ _____

Score   /20

35

Equivalent fractions

Learn and revise

A fraction, such as $\frac{2}{3}$, has two parts:

The **denominator** tells you the number of equal parts the whole is divided into. $\rightarrow$ $\mathbf{\frac{2}{3}}$ $\leftarrow$ The **numerator** tells you the number of those equal parts that are taken.

One part out of three shaded.

This shows $\frac{1}{3}$.

Two parts out of three shaded.

This shows $\frac{2}{3}$.

This fraction strip shows some equivalent fractions.

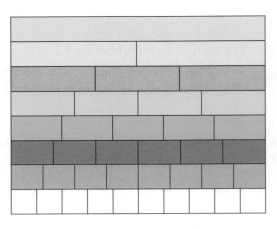

Use the strip to see that $\frac{1}{2}$ is the same as $\frac{2}{4}$ and $\frac{5}{10}$. What else is $\frac{1}{2}$ equivalent to?

Practice activities

1. Write the fraction shaded blue for each of these.

    a) 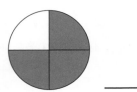 _____

    b)  _____

    c) 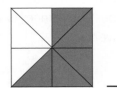 _____

    d) 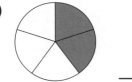 _____

2. Write the pairs of equivalent fractions shaded blue for each shape.

a)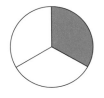

___ = ___

b)

___ = ___

c)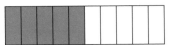

___ = ___

d)

___ = ___

3. Complete the next equivalent fraction in each of these.

a) $\dfrac{1}{2} = \dfrac{2}{\square} = \dfrac{\square}{6} = \dfrac{4}{\square} = \dfrac{\square}{\square} = \dfrac{\square}{\square}$

b) $\dfrac{1}{3} = \dfrac{\square}{6} = \dfrac{3}{\square} = \dfrac{\square}{12} = \dfrac{\square}{\square} = \dfrac{\square}{\square}$

c) $\dfrac{1}{4} = \dfrac{2}{\square} = \dfrac{\square}{12} = \dfrac{4}{\square} = \dfrac{\square}{\square} = \dfrac{\square}{\square}$

d) $\dfrac{1}{5} = \dfrac{\square}{10} = \dfrac{3}{\square} = \dfrac{\square}{20} = \dfrac{\square}{\square} = \dfrac{\square}{\square}$

37

Fractions of amounts

Learn and revise

When you need to find fractions of amounts, use the numerator and denominator.
When the numerator is 1, just divide the amount by the denominator.

Example:

What is $\frac{1}{5}$ of 10?

Divide 10 into five groups.

$\frac{1}{5}$ of 10 = 2

Practice activities

1. Colour $\frac{1}{4}$ of each group of fish. Write each answer.

    a)

    $\frac{1}{4}$ of 12 = _____

    b)

    $\frac{1}{4}$ of 8 = _____

    c)

    $\frac{1}{4}$ of 20 = _____

    d)

    $\frac{1}{4}$ of 16 = _____

2. Answer these.

    a) $\frac{1}{5}$ of 35 = _____   **b)** $\frac{1}{4}$ of 40 = _____   **c)** $\frac{1}{3}$ of 21 = _____

    d) $\frac{1}{6}$ of 30 = _____   **e)** $\frac{1}{10}$ of 70 = _____   **f)** $\frac{1}{3}$ of 33 = _____

3. Here are 20 oranges. Answer these.

$\frac{1}{5}$ of 20 = _____ $\frac{1}{2}$ of 20 = _____ $\frac{1}{4}$ of 20 = _____

Which would give you the greatest number of oranges, $\frac{1}{5}$, $\frac{1}{2}$ or $\frac{1}{4}$ of them?

_____

4. Look at your answers in practice activity 3. Is it true that $\frac{1}{2}$ is greater than $\frac{1}{4}$ and $\frac{1}{4}$ is greater than $\frac{1}{5}$?

$$\frac{1}{2} > \frac{1}{4} > \frac{1}{5}$$

True or false? _____

5. Complete these by writing < or > between each pair of amounts.

    a) $\frac{1}{6}$ of 30 ☐ $\frac{1}{5}$ of 30   **b)** $\frac{1}{3}$ of 15 ☐ $\frac{1}{5}$ of 15

    c) $\frac{1}{4}$ of 24 ☐ $\frac{1}{8}$ of 24   **d)** $\frac{1}{2}$ of 30 ☐ $\frac{1}{10}$ of 30

    e) $\frac{1}{10}$ of 40 ☐ $\frac{1}{5}$ of 40   **f)** $\frac{1}{3}$ of 18 ☐ $\frac{1}{6}$ of 18

6. Mr Jones has a total of 24 farm animals. Write the number of each farm animal he owns.

$\frac{1}{2}$ are chickens = _____ $\frac{1}{6}$ are cows = _____

$\frac{1}{4}$ are goats = _____ $\frac{1}{12}$ are ducks = _____

Fractions

Learn and revise

This number line is divided into tenths. They are written as common fractions (e.g. $\frac{1}{10}$) and as decimal fractions (e.g. 0.1).

$\frac{1}{10} = 0.1$ zero point one

$1\frac{2}{10} = 1.2$ one point two

The decimal point separates the whole number from the fraction.

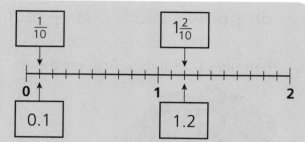

Practice activities

1. Write both the common fraction and decimal fraction for each arrow.

Example:

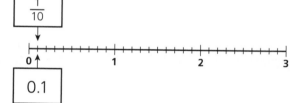

a)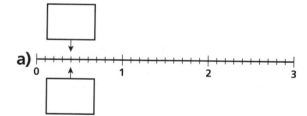

b)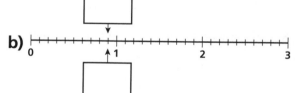

c)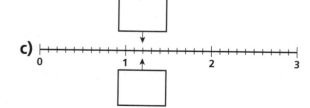

d)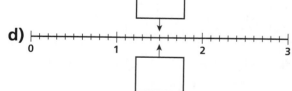

e)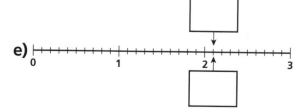

f)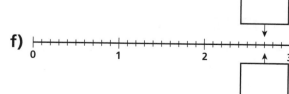

It is easy to add fractions with the same denominator – just add the numerators.

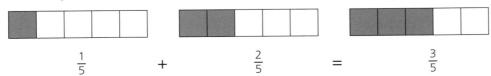

$$\frac{1}{5} \qquad + \qquad \frac{2}{5} \qquad = \qquad \frac{3}{5}$$

2. Add these fractions.

a)  $\frac{1}{4} + \frac{1}{4} = \underline{\hspace{1cm}}$

b)  $\frac{1}{6} + \frac{1}{6} = \underline{\hspace{1cm}}$

c) 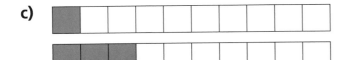 $\frac{1}{10} + \frac{3}{10} = \underline{\hspace{1cm}}$

d)  $\frac{1}{5} + \frac{3}{5} = \underline{\hspace{1cm}}$

3. Add these fractions. What do you notice? _____

a) $\frac{1}{3} + \frac{2}{3} = \underline{\hspace{2cm}}$

b) $\frac{1}{4} + \frac{3}{4} = \underline{\hspace{2cm}}$

c) $\frac{1}{2} + \frac{1}{2} = \underline{\hspace{2cm}}$

d) $\frac{2}{5} + \frac{3}{5} = \underline{\hspace{2cm}}$

4. Look at the fraction of each circle shaded red. Write these fractions in order, starting with the smallest.

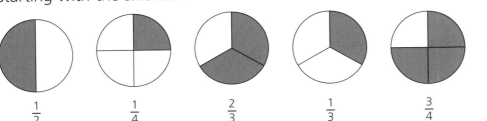

$$\frac{1}{2} \qquad \frac{1}{4} \qquad \frac{2}{3} \qquad \frac{1}{3} \qquad \frac{3}{4} \qquad \frac{1}{6}$$

____ ____ ____ ____ ____ ____
smallest

Mental arithmetic test 9

1.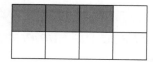

What fraction of the rectangle is shaded red?

_____

2. Shade $\frac{1}{4}$ of the rectangle blue.

3. Circle the fraction that is equivalent to $\frac{1}{2}$.

$\frac{3}{8}$ $\frac{3}{4}$ $\frac{2}{8}$

$\frac{4}{4}$ $\frac{2}{4}$

4. Write the next equivalent fraction.

$$\frac{1}{3} = \frac{2}{6} = \frac{3}{9} = \frac{\square}{\square}$$

5. What is $\frac{1}{4}$ of 20? _____

6. Complete by writing < or > between these amounts.

$\frac{1}{10}$ of 20 $\square$ $\frac{1}{2}$ of 20

7. Write $\frac{3}{10}$ as a decimal fraction. _____

8.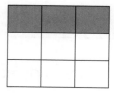

$\frac{3}{9} + \frac{2}{9} =$ _____

9. Circle the fraction that is equivalent to $\frac{1}{6}$.

$\frac{6}{10}$ $\frac{2}{3}$ $\frac{2}{12}$

10. Shade $\frac{2}{5}$ of this rectangle.

11. Write the common fraction and decimal fraction for the arrow.

_____ and _____

12. Write these fractions in order, starting with the smallest.

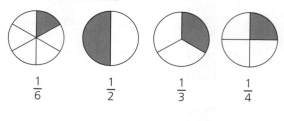

$\frac{1}{6}$ $\frac{1}{2}$ $\frac{1}{3}$ $\frac{1}{4}$

_____ _____ _____ _____

13.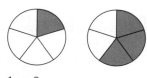

$\frac{1}{5} + \frac{3}{5} =$ _____

14. $\frac{1}{3} > \frac{1}{4} > \frac{1}{10}$ True or false?

_____

15. Complete this equivalent fraction chain.

$$\frac{1}{5} = \frac{\square}{10} = \frac{3}{\square} = \frac{4}{20}$$

16. $\frac{1}{10}$ of 50 = _____

There are 36 balloons in a pack. Write the number of each type of balloon in 17–20.

17. $\frac{1}{2}$ are red balloons = _____

18. $\frac{1}{3}$ are green balloons = _____

19. $\frac{1}{6}$ are blue balloons = _____

20. $\frac{1}{4}$ are large balloons = _____

Score /20

42

1. Shade $\frac{3}{4}$ of this rectangle blue.

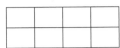

2. What is $\frac{1}{2}$ of 18? _____

3. Write the next equivalent fraction.

$$\frac{1}{2} = \frac{2}{4} = \frac{3}{6} = \frac{\square}{\square}$$

4. What fraction of this circle is shaded?

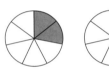

_____

5.

$\frac{2}{7} + \frac{2}{7} =$ _____

6. Write the common fraction and decimal fraction shown by the arrow.

1 ⊢——————↓———— 2

_____ and _____

A bag of 30 sweets are sorted. Write how many sweets of each flavour in 7–9, then answer 10.

7. $\frac{1}{3}$ toffee = _____

8. $\frac{1}{2}$ chocolate = _____

9. $\frac{1}{6}$ lemon = _____

10. Sam eats $\frac{1}{5}$ of the sweets. How many sweets does he eat?

_____

11. Write $\frac{7}{10}$ as a decimal fraction. _____

12. $\frac{1}{5} > \frac{5}{10} > \frac{1}{10}$ True or false?

_____

13.

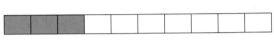

$\frac{5}{10} + \frac{3}{10} =$ _____

14. Complete by writing < or > between these amounts.

$\frac{1}{5}$ of 10 ☐ $\frac{1}{10}$ of 10

15. Circle the fraction that is equivalent to $\frac{2}{8}$.

$\frac{1}{2}$ $\frac{1}{3}$ $\frac{1}{4}$ $\frac{2}{4}$

16.

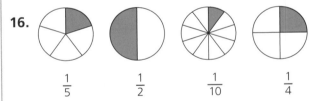

$\frac{1}{5}$ $\frac{1}{2}$ $\frac{1}{10}$ $\frac{1}{4}$

Write these fractions in order, starting with the smallest.

_____ _____ _____ _____

17. $\frac{1}{3}$ of 12 = _____

18. Write 0.6 as a common fraction. _____

19. Circle the greatest amount.

$\frac{1}{3}$ of 24 $\frac{1}{8}$ of 24 $\frac{1}{6}$ of 24

20. Complete this equivalent fraction chain.

$$\frac{1}{10} = \frac{\square}{20} = \frac{3}{\square} = \frac{4}{40}$$

Score /20

43

Measures

Learn and revise

You measure different things using different units.

You measure the length of objects in millimetres (mm), centimetres (cm) and metres (m).

10 mm = 1 cm

100 cm = 1 m

You measure the capacity of containers in millilitres (ml) and litres (l).

1000 ml = 1 l

You measure the mass or weight of an object in grams (g) and kilograms (kg).

1000 g = 1 kg

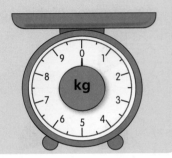

Practice activities

1. Join the matching lengths.

300 cm

1 m 20 cm

1 m 25 cm

3 m   125 cm   3 cm   120 cm

120 mm   30 cm   12 cm

300 mm   30 mm

2. Write the sign <, > or = to make each of these true.

a) 1 m 65 cm ☐ 165 mm

b) 2 m 40 cm ☐ 240 cm

c) 200 mm ☐ 2 cm

d) 60 cm ☐ 6 m

e) 18 cm ☐ 80 mm

f) 5 m 30 cm ☐ 530 cm

3. Mark the total weight on each weighing scale.

a)

| 3 kg | 3 kg |
| 3 kg | 3 kg |

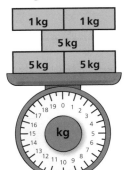

b)
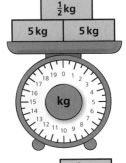

| | ½ kg | |
| 5 kg | | 5 kg |

c)

1 kg	1 kg
	5 kg	
5 kg	5 kg

d)

	½ kg	
2 kg	2 kg	2 kg
3 kg	3 kg	3 kg

4. Write the answers.

a) How many 200 ml bottles will fill a 1-litre jug? _____

b) How many 100 ml cups will fill a 2-litre jug? _____

c) How many 250 ml jugs will fill a 1-litre bottle? _____

d) How many 5 ml teaspoons will fill a 100 ml cup? _____

e) How many 500 ml bottles will fill a 2-litre jug? _____

5. Pipes come in two lengths: 50 cm and 90 cm long. They join together to make different lengths.

50 cm

90 cm

How many of each length would be needed to make a total length of exactly 3 m 30 cm? Draw a picture of joined pipes to show your answer.

Money

Learn and revise

These are the coins we use:

There are 100 pence in £1.

£1 = 100p

£2 = 200p

£1 and 50p = 150p

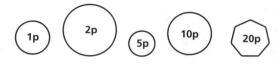

Practice activities

1. How much money is in each purse?

a)

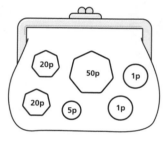

_____ p

b)

_____ p

c)

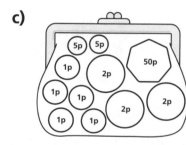

_____ p

2. Answer these.

a) A pencil costs 50p and you use four coins to pay for it. Which coins could you use?

_____

b) A ball costs 80p and you have a 20p coin in your hand. You use two more coins to make the total. Which coins did you use?

_____

c) A balloon costs 75p and you have a 10p coin in your hand. You use five more coins to make the total. Which coins did you use?

_____

3. Make up the following amounts with the fewest number of coins.

a) 85p _____

b) 124p _____

c) 99p _____

4. Amy buys these three items.

80p   60p   40p

What change will she get from £2? _____

5. What is the total cost of these items?

a)

One toothbrush costs 80p

× 5

Five toothbrushes cost: £ _____

b)

One toothpaste costs 60p

× 5

Five toothpastes cost: £ _____

c)

One soap costs 50p

× 4

Four soaps cost: £ _____

d)

One shower gel costs £2

× 3

Three shower gels cost: £ _____

6. Read the information and answer these questions.

- A bus journey to the National Park costs £3.
- Day tickets to the National Park cost £6.

a) How much does it cost for four people to travel on this bus? £ _____

b) How much does it cost for six people to visit the National Park? £ _____

c) How much does it cost for five people to catch the bus and also visit the park? £ _____

d) Children get into the National Park for half price. How much would it cost two adults and two children to visit the park? £ _____

e) An adult yearly pass to the park costs £48. How many times could you visit on a day ticket for the same price as the yearly pass? _____

Time

Learn and revise

There are 60 minutes in one hour. It takes five minutes for the minute hand to move from one number to the next.

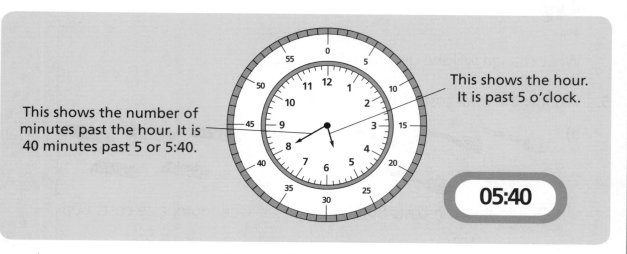

This shows the number of minutes past the hour. It is 40 minutes past 5 or 5:40.

This shows the hour. It is past 5 o'clock.

05:40

a.m. (ante meridiem) means before midday, so morning times.
p.m. (post meridiem) means after midday, so afternoon and evening times.

Practice activities

1. Write the times shown on each clock face.

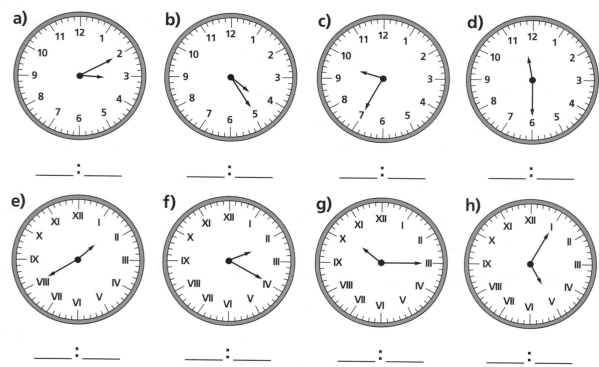

a) ____ : ____

b) ____ : ____

c) ____ : ____

d) ____ : ____

e) ____ : ____

f) ____ : ____

g) ____ : ____

h) ____ : ____

2. Draw these times on the clock faces. Write whether they are morning, afternoon or evening.

a) 4.05 p.m.

_____

b) 9.25 a.m.

_____

c) 11.45 a.m.

_____

d) 8.50 a.m.

_____

e) 2.55 p.m.

_____

f) 7.45 p.m.

_____

3. Draw the times half an hour later on these clocks.

a)

b)

c)

d)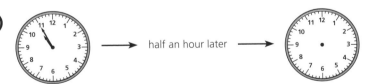

4. Complete these.

a) 120 seconds = _____ minutes

b) 3 weeks = _____ days

c) 4 hours = _____ minutes

d) 14 days = _____ weeks

e) $2\frac{1}{2}$ minutes = _____ seconds

f) $1\frac{1}{2}$ hours = _____ minutes

g) 4 years = _____ months

h) 600 minutes = _____ hours

Mental arithmetic test 11

1. A glass holds 250 ml. How many glasses can be filled from 1 litre of milk?

   _____

2. A purse contains six 20p coins. How much money is in the purse altogether?

   £_____

3. How many 500 ml jugs will fill a 3-litre bucket?

   _____

Look at the mug and spoon for 4–6.

70p   40p

4. How much does it cost to buy a mug and a spoon?

   £_____

5. How much does it cost to buy five spoons?

   £_____

6. How much change would you get from £3, if you bought three mugs?

   _____

7. Draw hands on this clock to show 11:25.

8. A cake costs 95p. Which four coins could be used to pay for it?

   _____ _____ _____ _____

9. $1\frac{1}{2}$ kg = _____ g

10. Read the weight on each of these.

    _____ kg   _____ kg

11. Three desks, each 150 cm in length, are put together to make one long table. What is the total length of this table?

    _____ cm

12. Write <, > or = for each of these.

    2 cm ☐ 20 mm   50 ml ☐ 5 l

13. Which three coins make 25p?

    _____ _____ _____

14. Write the time shown on each clock.

    _____   _____

15. 4 m = _____ cm

16. How much money is this? _____

17. Mark the correct weight on this scale.

18. How many weeks is a 14-day holiday?

    _____ weeks

19. Draw the time half an hour later.

    half an hour later

20. Which is longer, 18 cm or 81 mm? _____

Score   /20

Mental arithmetic test 12

1. Mark the weight on each scale.

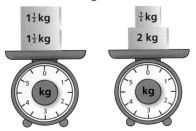

2. Write morning, afternoon or evening for each time.

8.30 p.m.   11.15 a.m.

_____   _____

3. How many 200 ml cups will fill a 1-litre jug?

_____

4. 3 m 50 cm = _____ cm

5. How many months are there in two years?

_____ months

6. Which four coins make 15p?

_____ _____ _____ _____

7. Medicine is given in a 5 ml spoon. How many spoonfuls will there be in a 100 ml bottle of medicine?

_____

Look at these clocks for 8–9.

8. Write the time shown on the first clock.

_____

9. Draw the time half an hour later.

10. How many 60 cm pieces of ribbon can be cut from a 3 m length of ribbon?

_____

11. 10 hours = _____ minutes

12. Circle the time that shows ten past eleven in the morning.

10.11 p.m.   11.10 a.m.

11.10 p.m.   10.11 a.m.

13. 40 mm = _____ cm

14. How much money is this? _____

15. 180 seconds = _____ minutes

Look at the cinema ticket and popcorn for 16–18.

£5   £2

16. How much will it cost five people to go to the cinema?

£ _____

17. How much does it cost for two cinema tickets and two packs of popcorn?

£ _____

18. How much change would you get from £10, if you bought one cinema ticket and one pack of popcorn?

£ _____

19. A book costs 50p. Which three coins could be used to pay for it?

_____ _____ _____

20. Write <, > or = for each of these.

60 cm ☐ 6 m   3 kg ☐ 3000 g

Score   /20

51

Speed test

- How many of these can you complete correctly in one minute?
- Write your answers on paper. Number them 1 to 40.
- Don't worry if you cannot answer them all, just answer them as quickly as you can.
- Stop after one minute, check your answers and record your score on the progress chart opposite.
- Then, try again at another time to see if you can improve your score!

Addition and subtraction

1. 6 + 3 = _____
2. 8 – 4 = _____
3. 5 + 2 = _____
4. 10 – 7 = _____
5. 9 – 3 = _____
6. 7 – 6 = _____
7. 4 + 4 = _____
8. 1 + 8 = _____
9. 10 – 1 = _____
10. 5 + 0 = _____
11. 12 + 3 = _____
12. 14 + 5 = _____
13. 17 – 6 = _____
14. 5 + 15 = _____
15. 18 – 3 = _____
16. 16 – 2 = _____
17. 1 + 13 = _____
18. 11 + 7 = _____
19. 19 – 5 = _____
20. 20 – 8 = _____

21. 9 + 2 = _____
22. 8 + 8 = _____
23. 5 + 7 = _____
24. 14 – 10 = _____
25. 12 – 4 = _____
26. 6 + 5 = _____
27. 14 – 7 = _____
28. 7 + 8 = _____
29. 11 – 2 = _____
30. 13 – 5 = _____
31. 4 + 9 = _____
32. 6 + 6 = _____
33. 12 – 6 = _____
34. 16 – 9 = _____
35. 3 + 8 = _____
36. 11 – 5 = _____
37. 6 + 8 = _____
38. 9 + 4 = _____
39. 14 – 4 = _____
40. 6 + 7 = _____

Progress chart

Colour in the stars to show your correct answers.

Scores out of 40

Attempt	1		2		3		4		5		6	
Date												
	39	40	39	40	39	40	39	40	39	40	39	40
	37	38	37	38	37	38	37	38	37	38	37	38
	35	36	35	36	35	36	35	36	35	36	35	36
	33	34	33	34	33	34	33	34	33	34	33	34
	31	32	31	32	31	32	31	32	31	32	31	32
	29	30	29	30	29	30	29	30	29	30	29	30
	27	28	27	28	27	28	27	28	27	28	27	28
	25	26	25	26	25	26	25	26	25	26	25	26
	23	24	23	24	23	24	23	24	23	24	23	24
	21	22	21	22	21	22	21	22	21	22	21	22
	19	20	19	20	19	20	19	20	19	20	19	20
	17	18	17	18	17	18	17	18	17	18	17	18
	15	16	15	16	15	16	15	16	15	16	15	16
	13	14	13	14	13	14	13	14	13	14	13	14
	11	12	11	12	11	12	11	12	11	12	11	12
	9	10	9	10	9	10	9	10	9	10	9	10
	7	8	7	8	7	8	7	8	7	8	7	8
	5	6	5	6	5	6	5	6	5	6	5	6
	3	4	3	4	3	4	3	4	3	4	3	4
	1	2	1	2	1	2	1	2	1	2	1	2

Speed test

- How many of these can you complete correctly in one minute?
- Write your answers on paper. Number them 1 to 40.
- Don't worry if you cannot answer them all, just answer them as quickly as you can.
- Stop after one minute, check your answers and record your score on the progress chart opposite.
- Then, try again at another time to see if you can improve your score!

Multiplication and division

1. 6 × 3 = _____
2. 8 × 4 = _____
3. 9 × 2 = _____
4. 28 ÷ 4 = _____
5. 8 × 8 = _____
6. 30 ÷ 5 = _____
7. 27 ÷ 3 = _____
8. 16 ÷ 2 = _____
9. 4 × 20 = _____
10. 8 × 3 = _____
11. 2 × 7 = _____
12. 4 × 6 = _____
13. 10 ÷ 2 = _____
14. 6 × 6 = _____
15. 3 × 70 = _____
16. 25 ÷ 5 = _____
17. 2 × 8 = _____
18. 40 ÷ 4 = _____
19. 4 × 4 = _____
20. 15 ÷ 3 = _____

21. 60 ÷ 10 = _____
22. 8 × 6 = _____
23. 9 × 5 = _____
24. 35 ÷ 5 = _____
25. 30 ÷ 3 = _____
26. 12 ÷ 2 = _____
27. 36 ÷ 4 = _____
28. 2 × 2 = _____
29. 9 × 10 = _____
30. 4 × 3 = _____
31. 40 ÷ 5 = _____
32. 20 ÷ 4 = _____
33. 70 ÷ 10 = _____
34. 6 × 6 = _____
35. 21 ÷ 3 = _____
36. 40 × 5 = _____
37. 2 × 80 = _____
38. 6 × 9 = _____
39. 20 ÷ 4 = _____
40. 30 × 2 = _____

Progress chart

Colour in the stars to show your correct answers.

Attempt	1	2	3	4	5	6
Date						

Scores out of 40

Attempt 1	Attempt 2	Attempt 3	Attempt 4	Attempt 5	Attempt 6
39 40	39 40	39 40	39 40	39 40	39 40
37 38	37 38	37 38	37 38	37 38	37 38
35 36	35 36	35 36	35 36	35 36	35 36
33 34	33 34	33 34	33 34	33 34	33 34
31 32	31 32	31 32	31 32	31 32	31 32
29 30	29 30	29 30	29 30	29 30	29 30
27 28	27 28	27 28	27 28	27 28	27 28
25 26	25 26	25 26	25 26	25 26	25 26
23 24	23 24	23 24	23 24	23 24	23 24
21 22	21 22	21 22	21 22	21 22	21 22
19 20	19 20	19 20	19 20	19 20	19 20
17 18	17 18	17 18	17 18	17 18	17 18
15 16	15 16	15 16	15 16	15 16	15 16
13 14	13 14	13 14	13 14	13 14	13 14
11 12	11 12	11 12	11 12	11 12	11 12
9 10	9 10	9 10	9 10	9 10	9 10
7 8	7 8	7 8	7 8	7 8	7 8
5 6	5 6	5 6	5 6	5 6	5 6
3 4	3 4	3 4	3 4	3 4	3 4
1 2	1 2	1 2	1 2	1 2	1 2

Speed test

- How many of these can you complete correctly in one minute?
- Write your answers on paper. Number them 1 to 40.
- Don't worry if you cannot answer them all, just answer them as quickly as you can.
- Stop after one minute, check your answers and record your score on the progress chart opposite.
- Then, try again at another time to see if you can improve your score!

Mixed problems

1. 10 × 3 = _____

2. 8 + 4 = _____

3. 19 – 2 = _____

4. 4 × 7 = _____

5. 16 ÷ 4 = _____

6. 6 × 5 = _____

7. 3 × 9 = _____

8. 7 + 7 = _____

9. 14 ÷ 2 = _____

10. 8 – 3 = _____

11. 12 – 7 = _____

12. 4 × 6 = _____

13. 20 ÷ 10 = _____

14. 6 × 6 = _____

15. 3 + 7 = _____

16. 11 – 5 = _____

17. 2 × 80 = _____

18. 13 + 4 = _____

19. 35 ÷ 5 = _____

20. 8 + 3 = _____

21. 7 + 6 = _____

22. 13 – 8 = _____

23. 18 ÷ 3 = _____

24. 4 + 7 = _____

25. 8 + 9 = _____

26. 15 – 6 = _____

27. 3 + 9 = _____

28. 5 × 5 = _____

29. 40 × 2 = _____

30. 8 + 7 = _____

31. 9 + 4 = _____

32. 11 – 6 = _____

33. 21 ÷ 3 = _____

34. 16 – 8 = _____

35. 8 + 6 = _____

36. 24 ÷ 4 = _____

37. 2 + 9 = _____

38. 10 × 4 = _____

39. 9 + 5 = _____

40. 8 × 3 = _____

Progress chart

Colour in the stars to show your correct answers.

Attempt	1	2	3	4	5	6
Date						

Scores out of 40

	1		2		3		4		5		6	
	39	40	39	40	39	40	39	40	39	40	39	40
	37	38	37	38	37	38	37	38	37	38	37	38
	35	36	35	36	35	36	35	36	35	36	35	36
	33	34	33	34	33	34	33	34	33	34	33	34
	31	32	31	32	31	32	31	32	31	32	31	32
	29	30	29	30	29	30	29	30	29	30	29	30
	27	28	27	28	27	28	27	28	27	28	27	28
	25	26	25	26	25	26	25	26	25	26	25	26
	23	24	23	24	23	24	23	24	23	24	23	24
	21	22	21	22	21	22	21	22	21	22	21	22
	19	20	19	20	19	20	19	20	19	20	19	20
	17	18	17	18	17	18	17	18	17	18	17	18
	15	16	15	16	15	16	15	16	15	16	15	16
	13	14	13	14	13	14	13	14	13	14	13	14
	11	12	11	12	11	12	11	12	11	12	11	12
	9	10	9	10	9	10	9	10	9	10	9	10
	7	8	7	8	7	8	7	8	7	8	7	8
	5	6	5	6	5	6	5	6	5	6	5	6
	3	4	3	4	3	4	3	4	3	4	3	4
	1	2	1	2	1	2	1	2	1	2	1	2

Key facts

Place value

Hundreds	Tens	Ones
7	3	8

700 > **30** > **8** >

738 = 700 + 30 + 8

seven hundred and thirty-eight

Comparing numbers

< means 'is less than'	> means 'is greater than'
102 < 120	234 > 209

Multiplication and division

×	1	2	3	4	5	6	7	8	9	10	11	12
1	1	2	3	4	5	6	7	8	9	10	11	12
2	2	4	6	8	10	12	14	16	18	20	22	24
3	3	6	9	12	15	18	21	24	27	30	33	36
4	4	8	12	16	20	24	28	32	36	40	44	48
5	5	10	15	20	25	30	35	40	45	50	55	60
6	6	12	18	24	30	36	42	48	54	60	66	72
7	7	14	21	28	35	42	49	56	63	70	77	84
8	8	16	24	32	40	48	56	64	72	80	88	96
9	9	18	27	36	45	54	63	72	81	90	99	108
10	10	20	30	40	50	60	70	80	90	100	110	120
11	11	22	33	44	55	66	77	88	99	110	121	132
12	12	24	36	48	60	72	84	96	108	120	132	144

Addition and subtraction

+	1	2	3	4	5	6	7	8	9	10
1	2	3	4	5	6	7	8	9	10	11
2	3	4	5	6	7	8	9	10	11	12
3	4	5	6	7	8	9	10	11	12	13
4	5	6	7	8	9	10	11	12	13	14
5	6	7	8	9	10	11	12	13	14	15
6	7	8	9	10	11	12	13	14	15	16
7	8	9	10	11	12	13	14	15	16	17
8	9	10	11	12	13	14	15	16	17	18
9	10	11	12	13	14	15	16	17	18	19
10	11	12	13	14	15	16	17	18	19	20

Measures

Length	1 metre (m) = 100 centimetres (cm)
	1 centimetre (cm) = 10 millimetres (mm)
Capacity	1 litre (l) = 1000 millilitres (ml)
Weight/mass	1 kilogram (kg) = 1000 grams (g)

Time

1 minute = 60 seconds

1 hour = 60 minutes

1 day = 24 hours

1 week = 7 days

1 fortnight = 14 days

1 year = 12 months = 365 days

leap year = 366 days

10:00   10:05   10:10   10:15   10:20   10:25

10:30   10:35   10:40   10:45   10:50   10:55

Acknowledgements

The author and publisher are grateful to the copyright holders for permission to use quoted materials and images.

P09 ©Tashsat; P52, 54, 56 ©Elmm

The above Images have been used under license from Shutterstock.com

All other images are © Letts Educational, an imprint of HarperCollins*Publishers*

Every effort has been made to trace copyright holders and obtain their permission for the use of copyright material. The author and publisher will gladly receive information enabling them to rectify any error or omission in subsequent editions. All facts are correct at time of going to press.

Published by Letts Educational
An imprint of HarperCollins*Publishers*
77–85 Fulham Palace Road
London W6 8JB

ISBN 9781844197309

First published 2013

01/040713

10 9 8 7 6 5 4 3 2 1

Text © 2013 Paul Broadbent

Design © 2013 Letts Educational, an imprint of HarperCollins*Publishers*

The author asserts his moral right to be identified as the author of this work.

All rights reserved. No part of this publication may be reproduced, stored in a retrieval system, or transmitted, in any form or by any means, electronic, mechanical, photocopying, recording or otherwise, without the prior permission of Letts Educational.

British Library Cataloguing in Publication Data.

A CIP record of this book is available from the British Library.

Commissioning Editor: Tammy Poggo

Author: Paul Broadbent

Project Manager: Richard Toms

Editorial: Amanda Dickson and Richard Toms

Cover Design: Paul Oates

Inside Concept Design: Ian Wrigley

Layout: Jouve India Private Limited

Production: Rebecca Evans

Printed in China

MIX
Paper from responsible sources
FSC™ C007454
www.fsc.org